Shopping with Gr

Story by Jackie Tidey
Photography by Lindsay Edwards

On Saturday,

Anya went to Grandma's house.

Anya's mum and dad
had to go to work.

"Goodbye, Anya," said her dad.
"Have fun with Grandma."

"Anya," said Grandma.

"Let's go to the market.

I have to get some food

for dinner on Sunday."

Anya and Grandma walked

all the way to the market.

At the market,

Grandma went from stall to stall,

and Anya helped her.

They got fish and eggs

and apples and bananas.

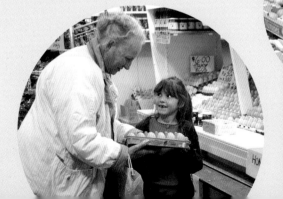

"Grandma, the shopping bags
are very heavy, now," said Anya.

"Yes," said Grandma.
"The bags **are** very heavy.
We can not walk home
with all this shopping."

"Look, Grandma," said Anya.

"We can get a bag with wheels, like that one."

"Clever girl!" said Grandma.

Anya and Grandma
looked for the bag stall.

Grandma got a big bag
with wheels.

ORDER NO.
STYLE NO.
COLOUR: *B*
G.W.
N.W.

"My new bag has lots of room
for shopping," said Grandma.

"Oh, no, Grandma!"
laughed Anya.
"Can we go home, now?"

"Yes," laughed Grandma.

"Let's go home."